SOLOS FOR JAZZ GUITAR

CLASSIC JAZZ SOLOS AS PLAYED BY:

DJANGO REINHARDT

CHARLIE CHRISTIAN

LES PAUL

TAL FARLOW

BARNEY KESSEL

WES MONTGOMERY

GEORGE BENSON

JOHN McLAUGHLIN

LARRY CORYELL

ANALYSES AND NOTE-FOR-NOTE TRANSCRIPTIONS BY FRED SOKOLOW

COMPLETE WITH A CATALOG OF JAZZ PHRASES BY EACH ARTIST

Compilation edited by RONNY S. SCHIFF

CARL FISCHER, Inc.

62 Cooper Square, New York, NY 10003

ATJ306   ISBN 0-8258-0399-3

CONTENTS

INTRODUCTION

The solos in this collection demonstrate the styles and techniques of major trailblazers of the jazz guitar. Jazz is always evolving, and major jazz artists—the ones that take the music a step further—always have a deep respect for the past; they know their musical roots. Charlie Christian studied and memorized Django Reinhardt's solos, Tal Farlow and Wes Montgomery (and many others) memorized Christian's solos, Larry Coryell studied Montgomery's work—that's how the music grows.

In the twenties, the four-string banjo was an essential rhythm instrument in a jazz band. Toward the end of the decade, with the introduction of the microphone, the guitar began to take the banjo's place. It was less brassy and capable of more subtle sounds. Thus, the first jazz guitarists were ex-banjo-players who strummed background chords, occasionally providing brief obbligatos to a vocal part. Even when soloing, guitarists of this era were very chord oriented.

Django Reinhardt may be considered the artist who signalled the beginning of the guitar's role as more than simply a chord-comping instrument. While Reinhardt was not the first guitarist to play excellent single-line solos, he exploded on the international jazz scene with such force that jazz—and the guitar—have never been the same since.

Most guitar innovators since Reinhardt have carried the guitar still further as a single-line soloing instrument. Les Paul was one of the first to amplify the guitar, which allowed the instrument to compete with horns, and Charlie Christian combined amplification with a sophisticated harmonic sense and gave the guitar a vocabulary relevant to bebop.

In the post-bebop era of the fifties, Barney Kessel and Tal Farlow built on Christian's foundation and played dazzling, contemporary sounding single-line solos—even though both players were firmly grounded in the chording school of jazz guitar as well. In the sixties and seventies, when jazz pioneers like John Coltrane, Herbie Hancock, and Bill Evans expanded the tonal possibilities of jazz, Wes Montgomery and George Benson developed single-line and octave soloing styles that allowed guitar to join or lead a "new" jazz ensemble. In the seventies, Larry Coryell and John McLaughlin led the way in the attempt to fuse the dynamic, apocalyptic rock sounds of that era with the complexities and subtleties of jazz music.

To study these solos, then, is to examine the directions jazz guitar improvisation has taken since the thirties. Keep in mind that the transcriptions that follow are not "tunes," they are improvised solos. And improvisation by a jazz master is more than the ornamentation of a written melody; it is spontaneous composition. Though each solo is based on a written "head" (a composed melody and chord progression), very rarely does the soloist even briefly allude to this written melody. The jazz improvisor spins new melodies over the given chord progression, taking inspiration from many sources: the texture and tonalities of the blues and other musical genres; licks and styles of other players, past and present; popular melodies from other pieces of music; and so on. There is also a playful experimentation with the physical capabilities of the instrument. Certain licks are natural and easy to play on guitar because of the tuning or general setup of the instrument, and the best players make use of them; but the same artists often seem to defy the guitar's limitations and play lines never heard before on guitar.

There will always be a new guitar stylist who takes the music and the instrument to new places. The important advances will be made by players who know their roots. That's one of the reasons I've assembled this collection of solos; to make the "history" more available to guitar students. I hope that in studying this music you can better appreciate and enjoy jazz guitar. You may or may not be the Charlie Christian of the next generation; either way, you'll have more fun playing and listening when you are familiar with the styles of the great guitarists.

EXPLANATION OF GUITAR SYMBOLS

 a **trill:** The even and rapid alternation of two tones a major or minor second apart. This example could be played:

 Slide up to the written note from a few frets back (usually from the next lower note in the scale).

 Slide from the first note to the second.

 Play the note, then **slide down** several frets and mute the string (this is a fast slide, used primarily for effect).

 a **bend:** Play the first note, then raise its pitch to that of the second note by choking or stretching the string.

 a **reverse bend:** Fret the second note and raise its pitch to the first note by choking the string before you strike the note; strike the choked string, then "let it down" to the pitch of the second note.

 a **hammer-on:** Play the first note, then "hammer on" to the second with another left-hand finger.

 a **pull-off:** Play the first note, then "pull off" with the left-hand finger, plucking the string and allowing the second note to sound.

 a **harmonic:** The diamond-shaped note indicates the actual pitch to be sounded.

 ghosted notes: These notes are played either so softly as to be nearly imperceptible or completely muted.

 vibrato: Play the note and shake the fretting finger.

Django Reinhardt
MINOR SWING

Django Reinhardt, the flamboyant Belgian gypsy with a crippled left hand, had a profound effect on Charlie Christian, Wes Montgomery, Chet Atkins, and nearly every other major guitarist that came after him. He was one of the pioneers of single-line soloing. In the early thirties, when he was playing with his famous Quintette du Hot Club de France, visiting American jazz players of the first magnitude sat in with him and returned to the States to spread his legend. His inventiveness, advanced harmonic sense, and swinging, playful, rhythmic style caught the attention of the jazz world and helped advance the guitar as a soloing instrument.

This solo from "Minor Swing," one of Reinhardt's best-known original instrumentals, shows why he had such an impact on guitarists: His playing *swung*, and he was a fountain of jazz ideas that never ran dry. Some typical Djangoisms in these solos (five times around the sixteen-bar progression) include:

- **Bluesy string-bending licks:** Reinhardt begins the first and third chorus with them, and they are sprinkled throughout the piece.
- **Octave soloing:** The fourth chorus begins with eight bars of octave soloing, which was a rarity in the thirties. Like the octave solos Wes Montgomery recorded decades later, Reinhardt's were rhythmic and percussive, and often emphasized jazzy intervals.
- **Jazzy intervals:** Years before bebop, Reinhardt made blue notes and flat and sharp fifths and ninths stand out in his solos. They are highlighted in the transcription, along with sixths, elevenths, and thirteenths. The flatted ninth at the end of the octave solo, and the flatted fifth in the eleventh bar of the fourth chorus are two shining examples.
- **Arpeggiated jazz chords:** Reinhardt played long, swooping eighth-note runs ornamented with trills and triplets. Often they were five or six bars long. Charlie Christian certainly imitated them. Many of these runs are arpeggios on extended jazz chords (e.g., E7b9+, Am9, and Dm6/9), and several of these are marked in the transcription. Often, in these several-bar-long arpeggio runs, Reinhardt seamlessly connected chords (see the two bracketed instances where Am6 turns into E7b9+).
- **Off-the-wall "guitaristic" licks:** Quirky licks, like the first-string riff that begins the second chorus, abound in Reinhardt's solos.
- **Interesting timing:** Once again, Charlie Christian must have taken note of Reinhardt's melodic runs that cut across bar lines and phrases that begin and end unexpectedly.
- **Repeated phrases:** Reinhardt invented short phrases and repeated them (with variations) over several measures; e.g., bars 9 through 12 in the first chorus.

Minor Swing

Django Reinhardt and Stephane Grappelli

Charlie Christian
AIR MAIL SPECIAL (I)
AIR MAIL SPECIAL (II)

Charlie Christian is widely acclaimed as the most influential electric jazz guitarist of all time. Nearly every post-Christian jazz guitarist cites him as the major influence and inspiration; a whole generation of guitarists—including Tal Farlow and Wes Montgomery—started their careers by memorizing Christian's recorded solos.

Christian was very visible during the years 1939 through 1941, when he played with the Benny Goodman band. Few guitarists before him played amplified single-line solos, and the fact that he could cut through the band like a horn was, in itself, a revelation to the jazz world. Besides being visible and amplified, Christian's solos were very swinging, inventive, improvisational, and harmonically advanced. During the same years when he was inspiring the Goodman band to swing harder, Christian was one of the regular afterhours players at Minton's in Harlem—along with Charlie Parker, Dizzy Gillespie, and Thelonious Monk. It is often said that bebop music coalesced at Minton's, and Christian was one of the architects of the style; his playing bridged the gap between swing and bebop.

The even, swinging eighth-note solos of "Air Mail Special" are typical of Christian's style. He played around with the rhythm—in all three solos there are two, three, and four-beat repeating phrases that cut across bar lines (many of these are bracketed in the music). This playful timing makes the solos fresh and exciting, as do the longer eighth-note runs that begin and end in unexpected places (some samples are bracketed in the music).

Throughout all three solos, Christian repeats three or four riffs that arise very naturally from the tonic chord played in this "F" formation:

They are marked in the music as A and B (the first three riffs are variations of the same phrase).

The D-sharp (E-flat) and B-flat in these riffs are "blue notes"—flatted thirds and sevenths. Christian's playing was always very blues-inflected, and the flat thirds and sevenths sprinkled throughout these solos are typical.

Christian, along with Django Reinhardt, was a pioneer in the use of passing tones or accidentals. His solos had a bebop flavor because he played a lot of flat and sharp fifths and ninths (and other higher notes of extended chords) and often made them stand out. Many of these "modern" intervals are noted in the music.

The use of augmented and diminished scales was another Christian trademark. He played augmented scales over a dominant seventh chord to lead to the chord that is a fourth higher (e.g., he played a G+ scale over a G7 chord leading to a C). He also played diminished scales to "lead up a fourth"; he often played the diminished scale a fifth above a dominant seventh chord (e.g., in a G7 to C passage he played a D^{o} scale over the G7 chord; this works harmonically, because a D^{o} resembles G7b9).

Since the bridge to "Air Mail Special" is mostly made up of diminished chords, these solos contain lots of samples of Christian's use of diminished scales. Interestingly, the last four measures of the second bridge imitate the end of the first bridge note-for-note, but the timing makes them sound different from one another.

Although the head of "Air Mail Special" is all tonic chord (C), during the "blowing" part of the tune the band plays the standard chord changes that are written in the solos that follow. These are loose and "unwritten"; they change from one solo to another, but all the soloists imply them. For instance, in the sixth measure of the first solo, Christian plays an Fm6 arpeggio over the F-leading-to-C passage (in a typical blues turnaround, the minor IV chord leads back to the tonic):

The solos that follow are transcribed from two different takes with the Benny Goodman sextet, recorded in 1940 and '41. As you play them, notice the inventive phrasing and timing that so enlivened Christian's improvising.

Air Mail Special (I)

Benny Goodman, Jimmy Mundy, and Charles Christian

ATJ306

Air Mail Special (II)

Benny Goodman, Jimmy Mundy, and Charles Christian

Les Paul
HOW HIGH THE MOON

In the mid-forties, Les Paul was one of the more prominent jazz guitarists in the business. Today he is as well known for his impact on the recording and guitar-making industries as he is for his playing. He designed one of the first solid-body electric guitars. A decade after he created it, the Gibson *Les Paul* became one of the most popular and most imitated electric guitars on the market, and it still is today. He also was the first to create multitracked recordings. The resulting sound was so revolutionary (and commercially successful) that Capitol Records touted it as "The New Sound."

In the early thirties, Les Paul worked at the Chicago CBS radio affiliate under two aliases: Les Paul, leader of the house band, and Rhubarb Red, hillbilly artist. In the mid thirties, he moved to New York, where, over the course of the next decade, he played with his own band and often appeared with Fred Waring and His Pennsylvanians. He also backed up popular artists like Bing Crosby, the Andrews Sisters, and Rudy Vallee. His work on network radio with Fred Waring helped popularize electric guitar (years before Charlie Christian played with Benny Goodman). In 1944, Paul appeared in the first of Norman Granz's "Jazz at the Philharmonic" shows. Five years later, he met and married singer Mary Ford. As a duo they created a series of hit jazz/pop records, including "How High the Moon." Through the use of multitracking, Les became a combo of from five to twelve guitars, and Mary an entire singing group! The overdubbed guitars were sped up and slowed down for even more special effects.

"How High the Moon" enjoyed a long stay in the number-one position on the charts in 1951. Paul's solo shows both the influence of Reinhardt and his own hillbilly roots. The intro and tag are multitracked and cannot be duplicated exactly on a single guitar. The entire lead solo is played in the key of G and sped up to the key of A which, coupled with an echo delay effect, gives the guitar an exaggerated, crisp attack and a unique, electronic sound. It also enhances the two trill figures:

Both these riffs are played entirely on the first string with hammer-ons and pull-offs. Notice how they overlap measures as they are repeated.

Other typical Les Paul techniques in the solo include bluesy double-stops on the first and second strings, bluesy "choked" (stretched) strings, muted strings, and a rhythm-chord section of the tune using triads on the top three strings. Notice that the solo contains musical concepts (like the trill of the double-stop) that are repeated over a series of measures. This is typical of pop studio players of later decades but was unusual in the late forties and early fifties when Les Paul created his "outer space" guitar sounds.

How High the Moon

Words & Music by Nancy Hamilton and Morgan Lewis

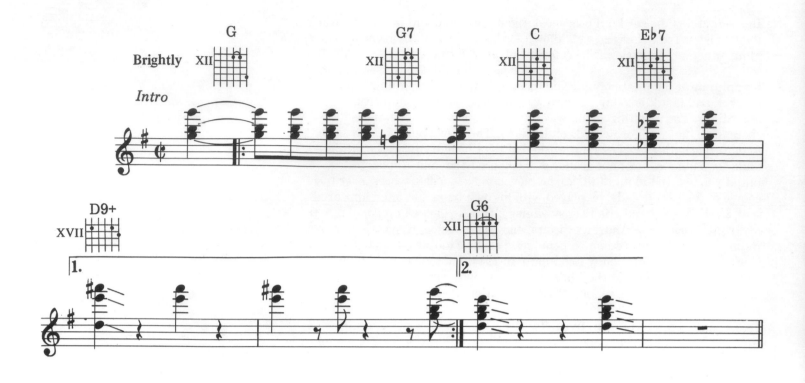

ATJ306

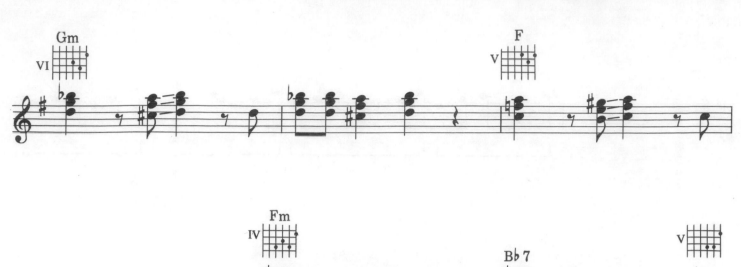

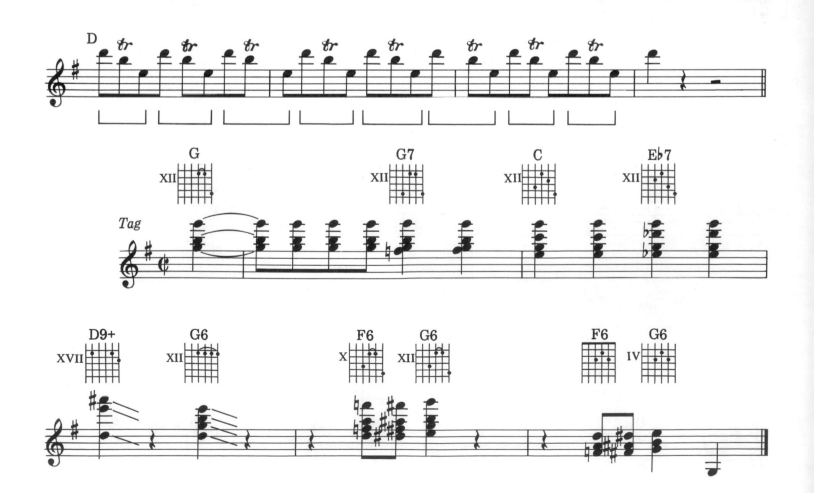

ATJ306

Tal Farlow
THIS CAN'T BE LOVE

Charlie Christian's playing inspired a very young sign painter named Tal Farlow to stop dabbling and get serious about the electric guitar. Farlow memorized many of Christian's solos, and before long he was gigging with various groups at New York jazz nightspots. During his years with the Red Norvo Trio, Farlow established his reputation as a fiery, innovative, and extremely fast single-note soloist. By the mid fifties, he was recording his own albums with top jazz players and was a guitar legend, and in turn, his speedy improvisational style inspired many other guitarists, such as Wes Montgomery and Larry Coryell.

A shy and reclusive man, Farlow has retired and "come back" several times. His performances and recordings continue to inspire and amaze the jazz world.

This solo, twice around the standard "This Can't Be Love," comes from a recording of the Red Norvo Trio album (with Charles Mingus on bass). It was recorded during a very fertile time in Farlow's career. The pace is very fast— almost hectic—and the sound is typical Tal. Farlow plays (and often accents) flat and sharp fifths, ninths, and elevenths, all of which give his soloing a bebop flavor. He also plays many chromatic ascending and descending runs, like these:

These arpeggios on a major seventh chord formation are sprinkled throughout the solo:

This phrase is played many times; Farlow probably uses a chord form similar to the above major seventh stretch (he has enormous hands):

The first eight or nine bars of the solo are almost duplicated at the beginning of the second chorus where Farlow plays similar notes with different timing. Still, his solo has lots of rhythmic and melodic variety.

Notice the substitute-chord arpeggios bracketed in the music: Farlow superimposes a Cm9 arpeggio over an F7 chord and an Ebm9 over an Ab, for example. Some parts of the solo sound odd when played slowly, but it all makes sense at breakneck speed!

This Can't Be Love
Words by Lorenz Hart. Music by Richard Rodgers

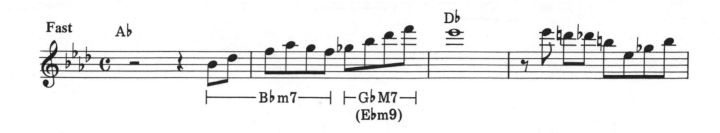

Bridge

Barney Kessel
EMBRACEABLE YOU

Barney Kessel, a self-taught guitarist from Oklahoma, came to Los Angeles in the early forties. After some years of touring with big bands (Charlie Barnet, Artie Shaw, Benny Goodman, and others), he soon became one of the top studio players for the recording, movie, TV, and radio industries. In the late forties, Kessel garnered public attention touring with "Jazz at the Philharmonic" and backing up such top jazz performers as Charlie Parker, Billie Holiday, Sarah Vaughan, and Lester Young.

In the early fifties, Kessel toured with the Oscar Peterson Trio and gained worldwide recognition. He began winning all the jazz polls and recorded with practically every jazz artist of the time. His own albums from this period helped the jazz guitar gain credibility as a lead instrument; on several LPs he led one of the first guitar/bass/drums trios. By the early seventies, Kessel had stopped most of his studio activity to concentrate on touring the world jazz circuit, composing, making his own albums, and teaching guitar seminars.

Kessel's single-line soloing is influenced by Charlie Christian; but he is perhaps more well known for his lyrical chord-style playing and his pretty jazz harmonies. He always swings and can be both funky and fiery in his solos, but that beautiful harmonic sense stands out.

This sample solo, from a 1955 Kessel LP, "To Swing or Not To Swing," is a single-line solo with a chord-style intro and ending. The introductory turnaround is typical of Kessel—it's pretty and it's cleanly executed. If anyone can sound improvisational and well thought out at the same time, Kessel does.

The single-line solo has a bebop feel reminiscent of Christian but with a freer, more contemporary rhythmic feel. Like Christian, Kessel varies his phrasing quite a bit and often plays passing tones in prominent places (see the many ninths, flatted ninths, elevenths, and flatted and sharped fifths indicated in the music). At the beginning of the solo, Kessel plays echoes of the original Gershwin melody with lots of embellishment. His solo then builds and becomes more complex and improvisational, and at the end, his brief chord solo alludes to the melody again.

ATJ306

Embraceable You
Words by Ira Gershwin. Music by George Gershwin

Wes Montgomery
FOUR ON SIX

Wes Montgomery burst onto the jazz scene with more impact than any other guitarist since Charlie Christian. His recordings, made from '57 to '68, display startling originality and powerful execution. Montgomery won more musical awards, received more critical acclaim, and sold more jazz records than any previous jazz guitarist. What made him unique as a guitarist?

His technique: Montgomery used his thumb instead of a flatpick, which gave him a unique sound and attack. Octave-soloing, his trademark, had been done before, but he used octaves with more speed and fluidity than ever before and played extended, highly developed octave-solos. His single-line solos and chord solos were also very original and just as technically complex and developed as his octave playing.

His ideas: Though Montgomery started his career playing note-for-note Charlie Christian solos, he soon began listening to horn players, especially Parker and Coltrane, for ideas. His playing was free from guitar clichés, and in terms of phrasing and harmony, he was probably the most fully realized—certainly the most original—post-bebop guitarist.

While many guitarists tend to build an extended solo by starting simply and gradually increasing in speed, complexity, and intensity, Montgomery often worked the opposite way: he would start with rapid single-line improvisation, progress toward less "notey" octave playing (often farther from the original melody), and end with still sparser chord soloing. He played abbreviated, three- or four-note chords on the treble strings and often created repetitious, rhythmic phrases reminiscent of big-band riffs.

The sample solos here are from a Verve recording of Montgomery (live at the Half Note in New York in 1965), stretching out on an original tune, "Four on Six." Throughout the octave solos he emphasizes the upper notes of extended chords: thirteenths, elevenths, minor ninths and sixths, and augmented and flatted fifths. (These are highlighted in the music notation; an arrow indicates that the note anticipates the next chord.)

In the first sixteen bars of the tune, Montgomery uses chords to punctuate the end of octave phrases. In the second sixteen bars, he plays a unique, percussive, rhythmic riff similar to the song's bass line; it accents the minor sixths and the ninths of a whole series of chords (labeled A).

The third time around the tune, still playing octaves, Montgomery performs a descending, sliding riff over a series of II/V changes (labeled B). His repetitious two-note riff consists of the eleventh and ninth of each minor II chord (or the tonic and thirteenth of each V7 chord), i.e., during the Cm to F7 measure he plays an F and slides down to a D.

Throughout the octave solos, Montgomery's phrasing is typically unpredictable, sophisticated, and ever-changing. He often anticipates the chord changes by half a measure (as, for example, in the riffs labeled A and B).

The two chord-solos (twice around the sixteen-bar tune) typify Montgomery's percussive chordal attack and unusual phrasing. In the first four bars of the first solo, he climbs the fretboard with an ascending chord line; he plays a variation of the ascent in the second eight-bar phrase.

The first sixteen bars end with an odd comping/sliding chord riff (labeled C). The second time around the progression, he opens with a repeated two-bar phrase that sounds like a big-band brass-section figure (labeled D). He repeats the same figure at the beginning of the second eight bars. Notice the big-band phrasing throughout both chord solos. The sixteen bar solos are not all consecutive, so some of them begin with partial-bar pick-up notes.

Four on Six
Wes Montgomery

ATJ306

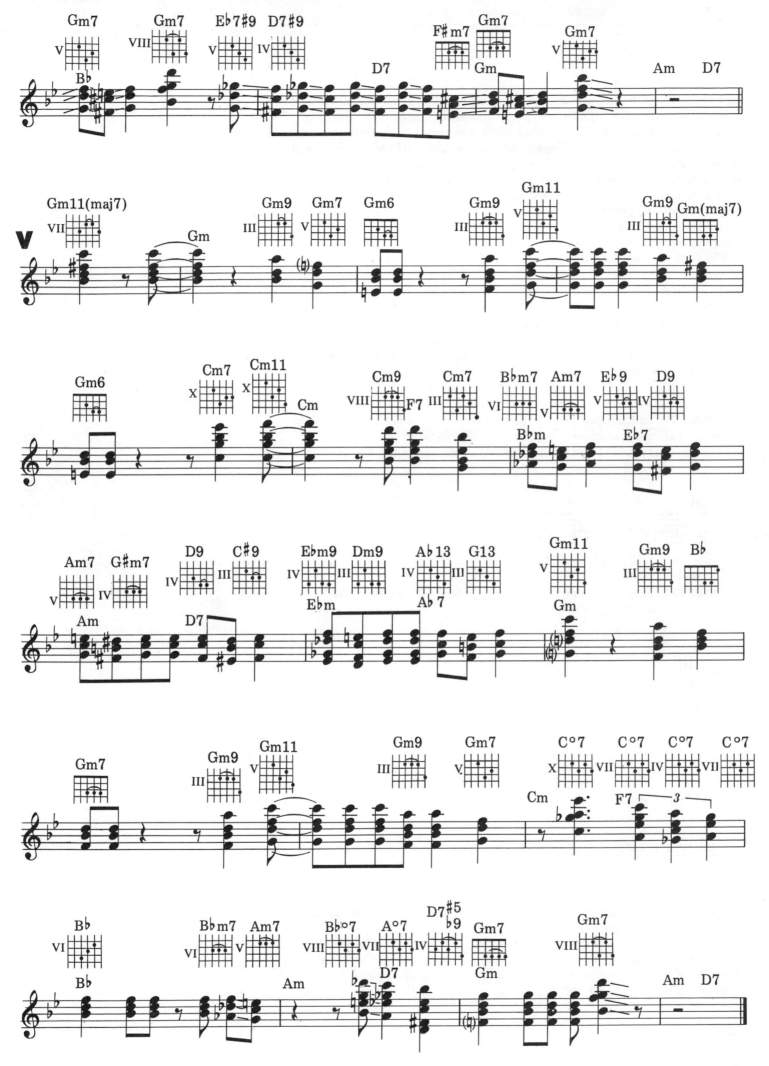

George Benson
SO THIS IS LOVE

In 1976, George Benson won all the jazz polls and was generally considered the world's leading young jazz guitarist; all this despite the fact that his then current, million-selling LP was much more pop and rhythm-and-blues oriented than his earlier jazz albums. Today, Benson continues to turn out pop/vocal hit records, but he plays enough guitar on each album (and in concert) to reaffirm his standing as the premier living jazz guitarist in the Charlie Christian tradition. His single-line solos are dazzling in their speed and strength; his playing combines contemporary jazz harmonies with a strong rhythm-and-blues flavor (as did Charlie Christian's solos); and he has his own warm, instantly recognizable sound.

The first records Benson remembers hearing were the Charlie Christian/Benny Goodman sides. At the age of eight, he played the ukulele, sang, and danced in nightclubs with his father. At seventeen, Benson led his own R&B group; a few years later he joined R&B/jazz organist Jack McDuff. After three years with McDuff, Benson made a series of jazz LPs that eventually established him as a leading player. Before his more pop-oriented Warner Brothers records were released, he had already recorded and performed with such influential jazz voices as Stanley Turrentine, Miles Davis, Hank Crawford, Freddie Hubbard, and Herbie Hancock.

The transcription that follows is Benson's solo on a one-chord vamp in his own tune, "So This Is Love." The song appeared on the 1976 *Breezin'* LP that catapulted Benson to pop stardom. Most of the solo (after the octave introduction) is played from these blues/rock positions in the key of E:

Occasional runs and arpeggios are based on an F-formation D triad,

or on a sliding pentatonic scale,

. . . or on the above blues/rock position in the key of B. All these departures from the E blues position are noted in the music.

The sections marked *A* are typical Benson repeating riffs. The *B* sections are chromatic runs Benson liberally sprinkles throughout the solo; these are also typical of his style. Note the amazing, rapid two-bar-long run that begins eight measures before the solo's end.

34

So This Is Love

George Benson

Funky, "half-time" rock beat

D triad (B)

ATJ306

© Communicated Music Co. 1977

35

D triad

B blues scale

sliding scale

John McLaughlin
BIRDS OF FIRE (I)
BIRDS OF FIRE (II)

Born in England into a musical family, John McLaughlin's early schooling included the study of classical and jazz music. His first professional work was with some of England's top pop artists, including Georgie Fame, Eric Clapton, Jack Bruce, and Graham Bond's seminal blues/rock band, The Graham Band Organisation. McLaughlin's jazz experiments with bassist Dave Holland and other avant-garde players brought him to the attention of drummer Tony Williams, and toward the end of the sixties, McLaughlin came to the U.S. to join Williams' Lifetime, the band that practically invented fusion music. It was also during this period that McLaughlin recorded with Miles Davis, creating albums that forever changed the course of jazz music.

By the early seventies, McLaughlin had created his Mahavishnu Orchestra, an ideal vehicle for the music he had expressed with Lifetime and Miles. The group did much to spread fusion music—improvisational jazz with intense rock and funk grooves plus screaming R&B based guitar and synthesizer. When the Orchestra disbanded in 1975, McLaughlin went on to form Shakti, a band that incorporated Eastern sounds into jazz music. Since then he has formed and/or participated in several ensembles, playing both acoustic and electric guitar, and blending jazz, R&B, and Eastern sounds.

The transcription that follows is from a Mahavishnu Orchestra recording of a McLaughlin composition. Typically, the piece has a challenging 9/4 time signature. Propelled by Billy Cobham's pounding, relentless drums, the feel is two bars of straight-four rock with an extra beat at the end of the second bar. There are no chord changes in the usual sense, only two droning flat-five chords:

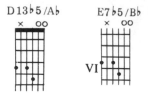

This allows for a lot of variation in key, but most of McLaughlin's soloing is of an "E-blues" nature. In fact, the majority of McLaughlin's fiery, intense soloing is based on the typical blues/rock scale shown below:

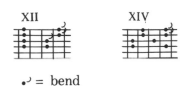

♪ = bend

Throughout these solos, the guitar has a typical rock sound: a lot of distortion, string-bending ("choking") and vibrato (produced by shaking the fretting finger, and indicated by a wavy line over the note ♪)—dynamic rock guitar!

McLaughlin often repeats a four- or five-note phrase over and over, varying it slightly, usually overlapping bar lines; these phrases are indicated by a circled *A* in the transcription.

At one point (labeled *B*), McLaughlin plays arpeggios based on the two flat-five drone chords. Rhythmic and tonal surprises occur throughout both solos, and the intensity and drive in his playing never lets up.

Birds of Fire (I)

John McLaughlin

Driving funk-rock beat

A blues scale

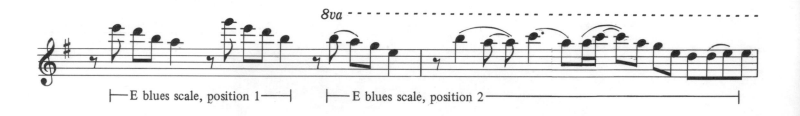

E blues scale, position 1

E blues scale, position 2

E blues scale, position 1

E blues scale, position 1

ATJ306

E blues scale, positon 2

E blues scale, positon 1

E blues scale, position 2

E blues scale, positon 1

E blues scale, position 2

Birds of Fire (II)

John McLaughlin

C# blues scale, position 1

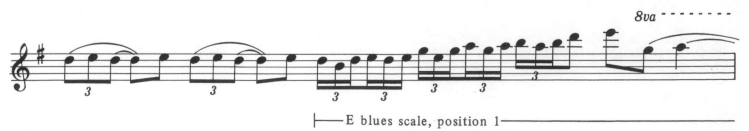

E blues scale, position 1

ATJ306

Larry Coryell
TORONTO UNDER THE SIGN OF CAPRICORN

Larry Coryell is one of the original jazz/rock fusion players, so it is not surprising to learn that his early influences were diverse: Chuck Berry, Chet Atkins, and Wes Montgomery. His first major job as a jazz guitarist was with Chico Hamilton's quintet, but it was when he joined vibist Gary Burton's eclectic quartet in the late sixties that Coryell's originality and amazing facility gained recognition. He later achieved prominence as a pioneer of electric jazz/rock guitar with his own group, the Eleventh House.

In the late seventies and early eighties, Coryell concentrated on acoustic guitar, playing solo and with several duos (he has teamed up for tours and LPs with Steve Khan and Philip Catherine). Whether playing acoustic or electric guitar, Coryell always displays dexterity and technical skill and knowledge in his playing; at the same time, he's a very emotional and spontaneous player.

The transcription that follows is from a 1978 recording of a solo acoustic performance in Europe. The long, rambling introduction includes many Coryell trademarks: dazzling, speedy runs that keep changing keys or modes in mid-stream; angular, unpredictable melodic shifts; twists and turns; the use of artificial harmonics; the overall spontaneous and experimental feel.

The two- and four-bar (and occasionally longer) phrases under the tempo marking "Bright rock ballad" occur later in the piece, when Coryell has established a definite rhythmic feel. He vamps on the Em and F#m chords shown below (having settled into a key at last!) and interjects short bursts of octave, single-note, and chordal improvisation while vamping. Here are the two patterns he uses for vamping (the rhythm gets busier and more intense as he builds the solo):

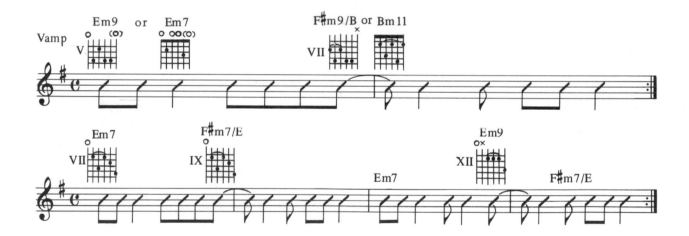

Coryell plays a lot of "guitaristic" phrases and patterns, i.e., musical figures that occur very naturally on the guitar. These are marked A in the transcription. In many of these instances, he executes a short lick and moves it around from string to string or up a few frets and back creating interesting key changes as he goes.

A note about the artificial harmonics in bars 26 and 27: The circled numbers beneath the notes tell you which strings to play; the number beneath the circle tells you which fret to touch for the harmonic note. The arpeggio in bar 26 alternates harmonics and "normal" notes; Coryell frequently uses this technique to achieve a pretty, harplike sound.

Toronto Under the Sign of Capricorn
Larry Coryell

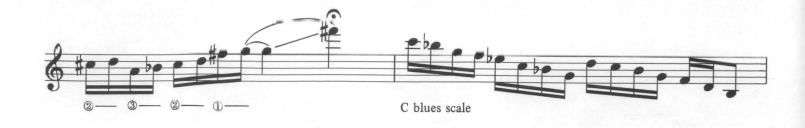

C blues scale

art.
harm.

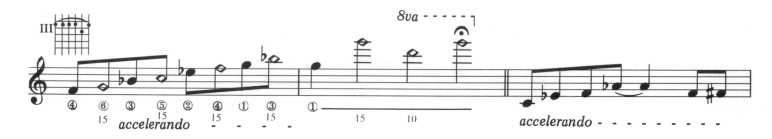

ATJ306

CATALOGUE OF PHRASES
ON V-I and II-V-I PROGRESSIONS

1

a.
Les Paul

b.
Barney Kessel

c.
Barney Kessel

d.
Barney Kessel

e.
Wes Montgomery

f.
Wes Montgomery

g.
Wes Montgomery

ATJ306

a.

Wes Montgomery

Am   D7

b.

E7   Am   *Barney Kessel*   D7

c.

Em7♭5   A7   *Barney Kessel*   Dm

a.

Django Rheinhardt

E7   Am   E7   Am

b.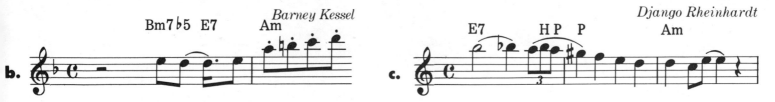

Bm7♭5   E7   *Barney Kessel*   Am   E7   H P P   *Django Rheinhardt*   Am

c.

d.

E7   *Django Rheinhardt*   Am   H P E7   Am

e.

E7   Am   E7   Am   *Django Rheinhardt*

f.

E7   Am   E7   Am   *Django Rheinhardt*

5

6

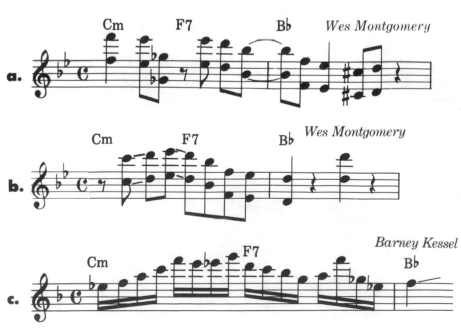

ATJ:306

7

Stylistic and Idiomatic Elements

George Benson

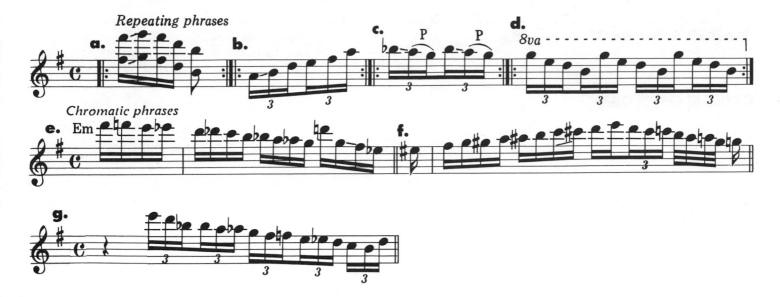

John McLaughlin

Larry Coryell

DISCOGRAPHY

DJANGO REINHARDT	Minor Swing	"The Legendary Django Reinhardt and the Quintet of the Hot Club of France" *GNT/Crescendo GNT9039*
CHARLIE CHRISTIAN	Air Mail Special	"Solo Flight—The Genius of Charlie Christian" *Columbia G30779 (1972)* *[(Originally released as Columbia WC026942 (1940) and CO29943 (1941)]*
LES PAUL	How High the Moon	"Les Paul/Mary Ford—The World Is Still Waiting for the Sunrise" *Capitol SM11308* *[(Originally released as a 78: Capitol 6958 (1951)]*
TAL FARLOW	This Can't Be Love	"The Red Norvo Trio with Tal Farlow and Charles Mingus" *Savoy 2212 (1976)* *[(Originally released as Savoy 12088/93 (1951)]*
BARNEY KESSEL	Embraceable You	"To Swing or Not to Swing" *Contemporary C3513 (1955)*
WES MONTGOMERY	Four on Six	"Willow Weep for Me" *Verve V68765 (1965)*
GEORGE BENSON	So This Is Love	"Breezin' " *Warner Brothers WB-BS2919*
JOHN McLAUGHLIN	Birds of Fire	"The Best of the Mahavishnu Orchestra" *Columbia PC36394 (1980)* *[(Originally released as "Birds of Fire" Columbia PC31996 (1973)]*
LARRY CORYELL	Toronto Under the Sign of Capricorn	"European Impressions" *Arista AN3005 (1978)*

ATJ306